Slide Do
the Rainbow

Collected by Pie Corbett
Illustrated by Diana Catchpole

Collins *Educational*
An imprint of HarperCollins*Publishers*

CONTENTS

If this book should dare to roam,
Box its ears and send it home.

Slide down the rainbow

See, see my baby,
I cannot play with you.
My sister's got the mumps,
My brother's got the flu.

Slide down the rainbow,
I'll slam the door.
See you round the back
At half past four.

Little Miss Muffet

Little Miss Muffet
Sat on a tuffet,
Eating some Irish stew.
There came a big spider
That sat down beside her
And so she ate him up too.

The boy stood on the burning deck

The boy stood on the burning deck,
His feet were full of blisters.
The flames came up and burned his pants,
So now he wears his sister's.

Humpty Dumpty

Humpty Dumpty sat on a wall,
Eating green bananas.
Where do you think he put the skins?
Down the King's pyjamas!

Twinkle, twinkle

Twinkle, twinkle chocolate bar,
Your Dad drives a rusty car.
Press the starter,
Pull the choke,
Off he goes in a cloud of smoke.

Toot! Toot!

A peanut sat on the railway line,
His heart was all a-flutter.

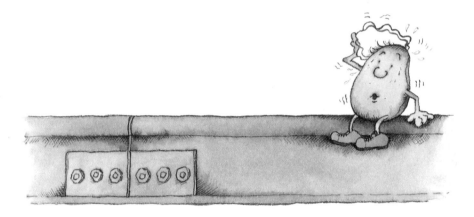

Along came Engine Number Nine.
Toot! Toot! Peanut butter!

Peas with honey

I eat my peas with honey,
I've done it all my life.
It makes the peas taste funny
But it keeps them on the knife.

In the garden

I was in the garden,
Picking beans and peas.

I dropped them all from laughing
When I heard a chicken sneeze!

Ice cream

I scream,
You scream,
We all scream
For ICE CREAM!

Row, row, row your boat

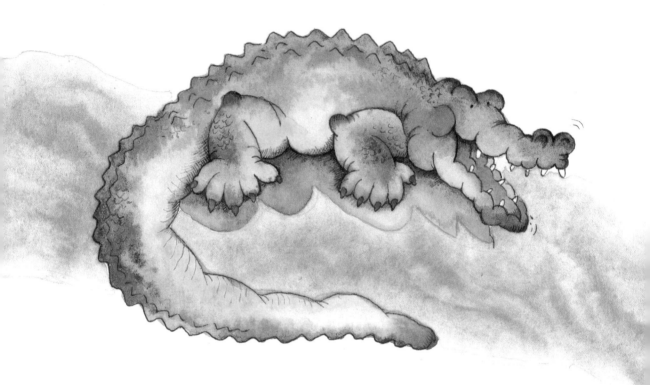

Row, row, row your boat,
Gently down the stream.
If you see a crocodile,
Don't forget to scream.
Aaaaargh!

Row, row, row your boat,
Gently down the stream.
Kick your teacher overboard
And see how loud she screams.
Aaaaargh!

I said my pyjamas

I said my pyjamas,
I slipped on my prayers.
I went up my slippers,
I took off the stairs.
I turned off the bed,
I jumped in the light.
The reason for this...
You gave me a fright!

Happy birthday

Happy birthday to you,
Squashed tomatoes and stew.
Bread and butter in the gutter,
Happy birthday to you!

Braces

Never let your braces dangle,
When you're standing by a mangle.

Mrs White

Mrs White
Had a fright
In the middle
Of the night
Saw a ghost
Eating toast
Half-way up
A lamp post.

Thank you

Thank you for the photo,
It was really nice.
I've put it in the attic
To scare away the mice.

The elephant

The elephant's a pretty bird,
It flits from bough to bough.

It builds its nest in a rhubarb tree
And whistles like a cow.

A bug and a flea

A bug and a flea
Went to sea,
On a reel of cotton.
The bug was drowned,
The flea was found
Stuck to a mermaid's bottom!

Way down South

Way down South where bananas grow
An ant stepped on an elephant's toe.
The elephant cried, with tears in his eyes,
"Pick on someone your own size!"

Three little monkeys

Three little monkeys
Jumping on the bed.
One fell off
And banged his head.
Momma called the doctor.
The doctor said,
"No more monkeys
Jumping on the bed."

By hook or by crook,
I'll be last in this book.